Love of My Life

by
Linda Kita-Bradley

Grass Roots Press

Love of My Life is published by
Grass Roots Press, a division of Literacy Services of Canada Ltd.

www.grassrootsbooks.net

ACKNOWLEDGMENTS

We acknowledge the financial support of the Government of Canada through the Canada Book Fund (CBF) for our publishing activities.

Produced with the assistance of the Government of Alberta, Alberta Multimedia Development Fund.

Government of Alberta ■

Editor: Dr. Pat Campbell
Photography: Grass Roots Press
Book design: Lara Minja, Lime Design Inc.

Library and Archives Canada Cataloguing in Publication

Kita-Bradley, Linda, 1958–
    Love of my life / Linda Kita-Bradley.

ISBN 978–1–926583–87–-7

    1. Readers for new literates. 2. Readers—Older couples. I. Title.

PE1126.N43K5855 2012   428.6'2   C2012–902993–9

This is Don and Dell.

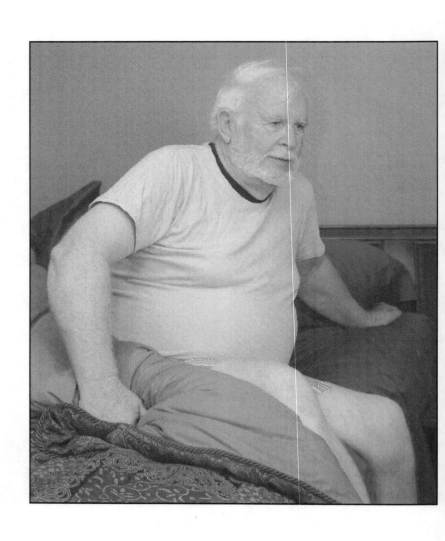

Don gets up.

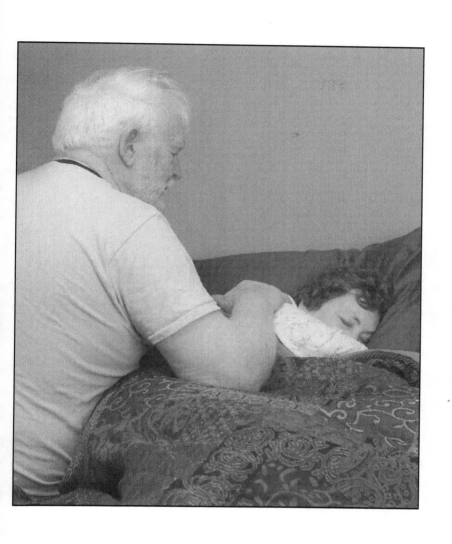

He sits beside Dell.

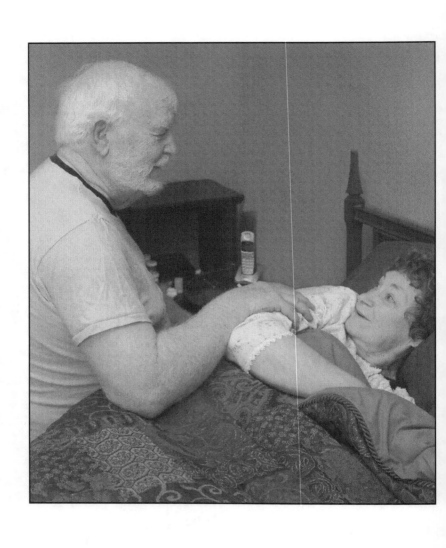

Don says, "Dell. Time to get up."

Don makes tea.

Don makes toast.

Don and Dell eat.

They go for a walk.

Don drives Dell to the store.

Don waits in the car.

Dell makes lunch.

She makes soup.

She makes salad.

She makes tea.

Don and Dell eat.

They wash the dishes.

Don takes a nap.

Dell takes a nap.

They work in the yard.

They play cards after dinner.

They go to bed.

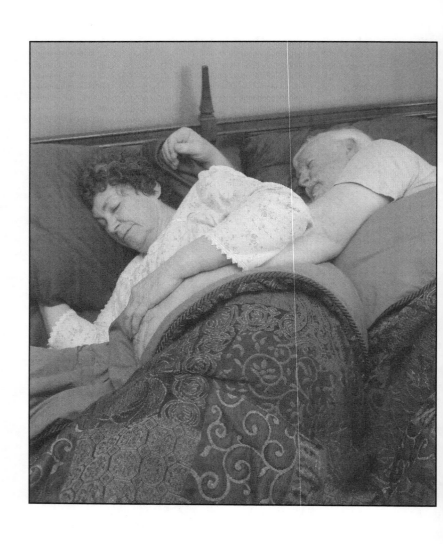

They sleep.

Made in the USA
Las Vegas, NV
14 March 2024

87201626R00015